FUN GANG BOOKS

This
Fun Gang Picture Book
Belongs to

....

Who Is McBlackbeard?

Once upon a time there was a pirate called Blackbeard who used to sail the high seas capturing treasure wherever he could.

Blackbeard was the scariest of all pirates that ever lived.

On his ship there were cannons, a huge anchor and a very tall mast with a flag called the Jolly Roger.

The flag had a skull and crossbones on it.

If you see a ship with the Jolly Roger, then you should...

RUN as fast as you can or SWIM as fast as possible.

Or just shout HELP!

Every Pirate Needs A Map

But now there is ANOTHER pirate who is a cousin of Blackbeard.
HIS name is McBlackbeard and he is a FRIENDLY pirate.

He lives in Scotland and he does GOOD things.
He is also learning to play the BAGPIPES.

Let's see what he is doing today!

and the
Highland Games

Gerry Ogilvie
Hovhannes Yedigaryan

ISBN: 978-1-5272-8016-8

Made in UK

Today McBlackbeard is excited.

He has received a letter from the Queen.

It's an invitation to play his bagpipes at the famous
Balmoral Highland Games in Scotland.

He remembers hearing all about last year's Games
where sisters Maggie and Aggie won every event.

He has always wanted to go to the Highland Games
and can't believe he's been asked to play
his bagpipes there.

...But he has to be there this afternoon.

McBlackbeard quickly gets ready
and packs his bagpipes.

Farmer McDonald gives him a lift to the station in his **shoogly, shaky** tractor.

Soon, McBlackbeard is speeding towards the Highland Games.

Farmer McDonald waves him good luck!

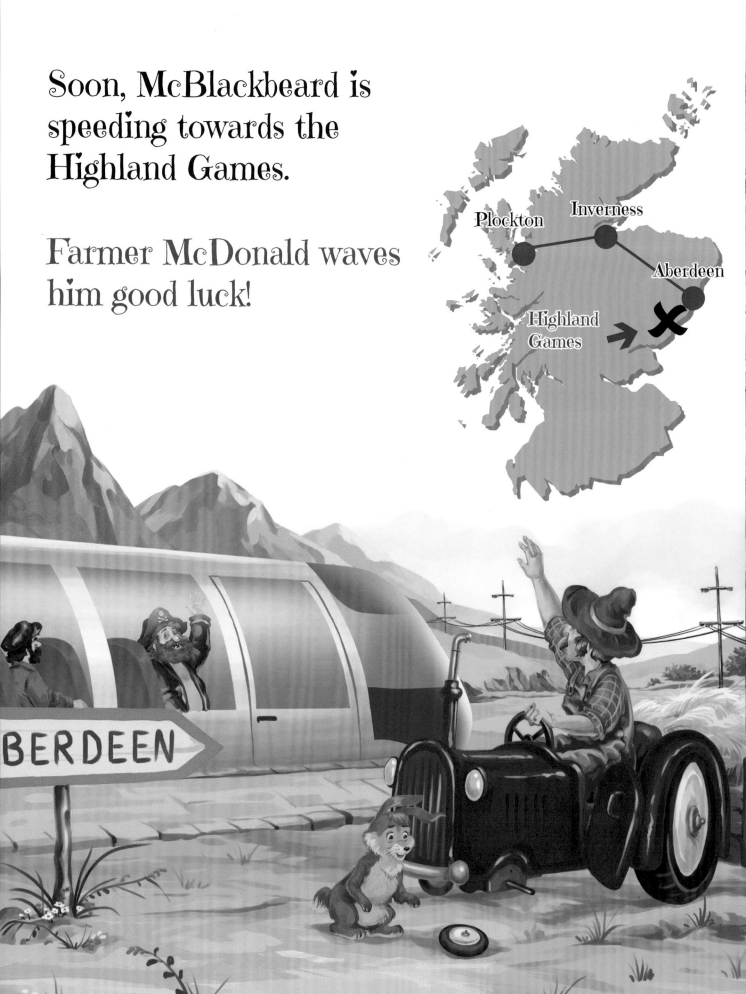

As McBlackbeard arrives at the large stadium,
he is amazed to see so many people.
The crowds are

HUGE.

Everyone is rushing and pushing to get the best seats and
McBlackbeard falls over in the scramble. Even his bagpipes get
stood on and they let out a wail and a groan.

McBlackbeard cleans himself off and gets ready
to play his bagpipes.

Suddenly, a huge roar comes from the crowd
and they stand up cheering.

The Queen is arriving and McBlackbeard plays

Scotland The Brave.

As she passes in her carriage, the Queen gives
McBlackbeard a wave and she smiles.
McBlackbeard feels very proud of himself.

After McBlackbeard finishes playing, a man in a smart uniform comes running towards him looking worried. The man has a piece of paper in his hand and he speaks in a very posh voice.

"Someone has taken ill and we are one person short for the events — the Queen would like you, McBlackbeard, to stand in as a replacement," he says.

"Tell Her Majesty the Queen I will be delighted," says McBlackbeard. However, McBlackbeard doesn't know anything about
THE HIGHLAND GAMES.

He starts to look worried.

"The first event is the Tug of War,"
the man announces.

McBlackbeard is now VERY, VERY worried.

His legs are shaking and his knees are knocking together.

The thought of walking out there in front of thousands of
people almost makes McBlackbeard feel sick...

and now things are about to get even worse!

McBlackbeard joins his team.

As they wait to begin, he notices two fierce looking women.
It's Maggie and Aggie... last year's champions!
They growl at McBlackbeard and give him a mean look.

"If you think you're going to win, then

THINK AGAIN!"

One of them snarls.

Suddenly McBlackbeard isn't frightened anymore.

He remembers that he is used to pulling ropes on his pirate ship. In fact, he has hoisted up the anchor a thousand times.

"I can do this," he laughs.

"And I WILL do it!

Nobody is going to scare me!"

"Are you ready?
...GO!"
the starter shouts.

They all pull this way and that way.
Everyone's faces are getting red with the strain of pulling.

Maggie and Aggie's feet are pushing into the mud.

McBlackbeard begins slipping forwards.
Then he imagines he is on his pirate ship.

He gives an extra tug just like he used to do with the anchor.
Maggie and Aggie lose their grip and fly backwards into the mud.

McBlackbeard's team win and Maggie and Aggie are so annoyed they have STEAM coming out of their EARS!

They are blazing mad!

The score is one nil to McBlackbeard.

The next event is Tossing the Caber.
"That's just a big pole,"
McBlackbeard thinks.
"Like the huge mast on my pirate ship.
You have to pick up
the pole and throw it."

Suddenly Maggie walks over to McBlackbeard and pretends to be friendly to him. But, while she distracts McBlackbeard, Aggie is kneeling down tying his laces together.

Uh-oh.... He doesn't notice!

McBlackbeard lifts the caber and gets ready to throw.
But as he runs forward, he trips on his laces.

He falls flat on his face in a huge puddle. There is a big

OOH and AHH

from the crowd.

Maggie and Aggie are laughing so much they can't speak.
They are bent double slapping each other on the back.

McBlackbeard is annoyed as he looks over at
the two of them. Maggie and Aggie look very
smug as they give 'high-fives' all round.

The score is now one all!

"The next event is the Shot Put,"
the loudspeaker blares loudly.

This is a very heavy ball made of metal.
Whoever throws it the furthest wins.

McBlackbeard looks at the ball.
It is just like a cannon ball from his pirate ship.
"I've lifted many cannon balls in my days as a pirate," he thinks.

As he picks up the ball, McBlackbeard is so focused
on winning, he doesn't notice Maggie and Aggie have
played another trick on him -

They have rolled the ball in cow dung from a Highland cow!

It is sticky, slimy and horrible.
Imagine - horrible poo from a Highland coo!

The smell is so bad even the Queen holds her nose.

McBlackbeard steps forward to throw, but the ball
slips out of his hand and falls on his toe.

"Ouch!"

McBlackbeard yells, hopping around.

His hands are all slimy from the cow poo!

Maggie and Aggie are laughing so much, Maggie's
teeth fly right out of her mouth.

But they don't care - because they are now leading 2 to 1 !

The last event is the High Jump.
McBlackbeard has never tried this in his life.
"I will be hopeless!" he thinks.

Maggie and Aggie used to be champion highland dancers. They were
also gymnastic winners. They are able to leap in the air very easily.

What will McBlackbeard do now ?

He looks over and sees Maggie and Aggie grinning
and looking very smug.

Suddenly, a huge gust of wind blows through the stadium.

The crowd

Then a terrible thing happens.

The Queen's hat blows away!

"Don't worry, Your Majesty!"

McBlackbeard shouts, as he begins chasing the hat.

The crowd cheer as McBlackbeard runs
after the Queen's hat.

They are now on their feet hoping
he will grab it.

McBlackbeard dives through a huge puddle to
reach it but the hat takes off again.

He runs this way...

and then that way!

As the Queen's hat lifts higher towards the sky, McBlackbeard takes a last magnificent leap.

He finally grabs the hat with his fingertips.

However, McBlackbeard doesn't notice he has leaped over the high jump at the same time!

He has broken the record for the best jump ever at the Balmoral Highland Games.

The crowd give a special roar and everyone cheers loudly.

How AMAZING is that?

As McBlackbeard takes a bow, an extra gust of wind
blows his kilt up in the air.

Everyone in the stadium can see
McBlackbeard's bum!

His face is red with embarrassment.

The Queen has to cover her eyes.

"Imagine the Queen seeing your bum?"
McBlackbeard thinks.

The Queen is so pleased to have her hat back she declares
McBlackbeard the Champion of the Highland Games.

Maggie and Aggie are disqualified for cheating.

They are boiling mad. Furious - Fizzing and Scunnered.

The Queen asks McBlackbeard to play
his bagpipes one more time.

As he marches around the stadium, the crowd roar
louder than all the bagpipes in the whole wide world.

Poor Maggie and Aggie...

Because they tried to cheat, the Queen orders them to pick up the rubbish that was blown all around the stadium.

"We'll be back next year!" shouts Aggie.

"See you here at the Highland Games."

Highland Games — Fun Facts

What are the Highland Games?

Imagine your School Sports day!

Then imagine it much BIGGER!

There is Running, Throwing, Highland Dancing, Lifting Heavy Things, Playing Bagpipes and Marching. Jumping, Sword Dancing, Tug Of War, Eating a Hotdog or Hamburger MMMM!

There can be races for all ages and even competitions for dogs and Highland cattle — a HIGHLAND COO — like in McBlackbeard's story.

Where are the Games?

Mostly in Scotland but also in hundreds of places all over the World! Russia, America, Canada, Switzerland, Australia, New Zealand, Bermuda and many more places.

In Scotland there are about 100 HIGHLAND GAMES each year.

Have you heard of any of these places?

Oban • Aberdeen • Stirling • Inverness
Loch Lomond • Burntisland • Perth • Isle of Skye

There are many places that have Highland Games. Can you find any more?

Can you name SIX TOWNS in Scotland where they have Highland Games? • Can you name SIX EVE

What are Bagpipes?

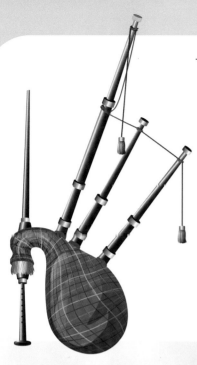

Bagpipes are a woodwind instrument.

You blow air through a small tube called the mouthpiece and into a bag (imagine a balloon filled with air - only much stronger).

The bag holds the air and it comes out through the chanter which is what your fingers play the tune on. Finally there is a deeper droning sound and these are three more pipes, called drones, resting on your shoulder.

Which part is the BAG? • Where is the CHANTER?
Where is the MOUTHPIECE? • Where are the THREE DRONES?

Things to do — Make your own Highland Games

Get a Wellington Boot and hold with both hands and throw it backwards over your head!

Try the Tug Of War with your friends

Get a tennis ball or something that size and then hold it near your SHOULDER and THROW!

Make a caber from cardboard or foam insulation pipe cover.
Make swords from cardboard for the Sword Dance.

Have FUN doing all these things!

he Highland Games? • Can you name SIX COUNTRIES of the World where they have Highland Games?

Word Search

How many of these words can you find in the story?
Some will be easier to find than others and you may know some words better than others.

Write them all first on a piece of paper then tick them when you find them.

Good Luck !

QUEEN   VERY   POSH   EARS   PUDDLE
CABER   GROAN   TEETH   SNARLS
HUGE   ROAR   HURRICANE   CHEERING
STEAM   HOISTED   BAGPIPES
AGGIE   AFTERNOON   SHOOGLY   UNIFORM
ANCHOR   HOTDOG   AMAZING
MAGGIE   HIGHJUMP   MCBLACKBEARD
WORRIED   LACES   SMUG   RED
FINGERTIPS   SCOTLAND   SCRAMBLE
STADIUM   SLIMY   CANNONBALL
WAIL   BELIEVE   TRACTOR   SHAKING
CHAMPIONS   HIGH-FIVES   GROWL

Here are **THREE** of the **BIGGEST** words in the story ...where are they?

EMBARRASSMENT   MAGNIFICENT   DISQUALIFIED

(what do they mean?)

Some TIPS on your words

Don't worry if you can't find every word - it's not that easy to see them all.
Don't worry if you don't know some of the words - sometimes if you don't know a word
then LOOK at the words around it to try and work out what you THINK it means.

Long words can often be split up into 2 or 3 parts like Hotdog (hot + dog)
— It helps you understand better.

Here are some more...
AFTERNOON (after + noon)
FINGERTIPS (finger + tips)
CANNONBALL (cannon + ball)
BAGPIPES (bag + pipes)

No one knows every word - so if you don't know a word then look it up

A strange word in our story is
SHOOGLY
Do you know what it means?

It means a bit SHAKY or LOOSE - like a chair with a shaky leg or you put
a key in a door and you need to 'shoogle' it — move it around to fit.
Or if you wake someone up you shake them gently - shoogle them.

Find out what some of the other words mean and
KEEP READING!

If you would like to write a story and maybe have it made into a book for your
SCHOOL then look at our website

www.kidzwriteforkidz.co.uk

A

Book

Designed by Fun Gang Books
Published 2021

The Fun Gang UK

Thanks to Sophie Mckinna - Champion Shot Putter